**2** Describe fully each of the numbered melodic intervals (e.g. major 2nd).

Beethoven,

Intervals:

1 ............................................................

2 ............................................................

3 ............................................................

4 ............................................................

5 ............................................................

**3** The following melody is written for clarinet in B♭. Transpose it *down* a major 2nd, as it will sound at concert pitch. Do *not* use a key signature but remember to put in all necessary sharp, flat or natural signs.

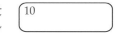

R. Strauss, *Der Rosenkavalier*

**4** The following extract is adapted from a piano piece, *Sicilianisch*, by Schumann. Look at it and then answer the questions that follow.

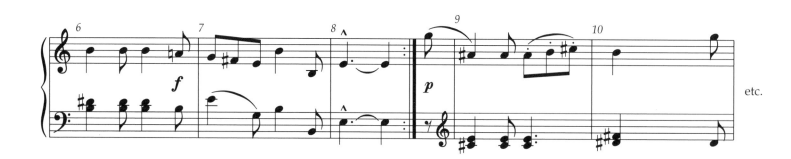

etc.

(a) (i) Give the meaning of:

10

     **Scherzando** ................................................................................. (2)

     ⌣ᐧᐧ (e.g. bar 1) ................................................................................. (2)

     ∧ (e.g. bar 4) ................................................................................. (2)

     :‖ (bar 8) ................................................................................. (2)

(ii) Describe the time signature as:   simple or compound   ...........................................

                                             duple, triple or quadruple   ................................... (2)

**ABRSM**

£ 3.25

# Theory of

# Music

# Exams

## GRADE 5

# 2008

# Theory Paper Grade 5   2008   A

*Duration 2 hours*

**This paper contains SEVEN questions, ALL of which should be answered.**
**Write your answers on this paper – no others will be accepted.**
**Answers must be written clearly and neatly – otherwise marks may be lost.**

15

**1**  (a)  Look at the following extract and then answer the questions below.

Gabriel Jackson, *Creator of the stars of night*

etc.

© Oxford University Press 2004
Reproduced by permission.

   (i)   The extract begins on the first beat of the bar. Put in the time signature at the
         beginning and add the missing bar-lines. The first bar-line is given.     (5)

   (ii)  Name the ornament (marked *) in the final bar.  .........................................................  (2)

(b)  Look at the following extract and then answer the questions below.

Haydn, Rondo for keyboard (from Hob. I/85)

etc.

   (i)   Describe the chords marked A, B and C as I, II, IV or V. Also indicate whether
         the lowest note of the chord is the root (a), 3rd (b) or 5th (c). The key is E♭ major.

     Chord **A** ............................  Chord **B** ...........................  Chord **C** ..................................  (6)

   (ii)  Write as a breve (double whole-note) an enharmonic equivalent of the last right-hand
         note in the extract.

                                      (2)

(b) (i) Give the technical names (e.g. tonic, supertonic) of the right-hand notes marked $\boxed{10}$
X and Y. The key is A minor.

X (bar 2) ....................................... Y (bar 3) ......................................... (4)

(ii) Add suitable rest(s) EITHER to the right-hand OR to the left-hand staves of bar 10 to complete the bar. (2)

(iii) Rewrite the **complete** first chord of bar 1 (right-hand **and** left-hand notes) so that it sounds at the same pitch, but using the tenor C clef. Remember to put in the clef sign.

(4)

$\boxed{10}$

(c) (i) Complete the following statement:

The right-hand notes of bar 5 form the dominant triad in the key of .............................. . (2)

(ii) Underline *one* of the following instruments that could play bars 7–8 of the left-hand part so that it sounds at the same pitch and name the family of orchestral instruments to which it belongs.

               flute          cello         side drum         oboe

Family ......................................................... (4)

(iii) Now name a *different* family of standard orchestral instruments and state the name of its lowest-sounding member.

Family ......................................................... Instrument ......................................................... (4)

**5** (a) Using semibreves (whole-notes), write one octave **ascending** of the **melodic** minor scale that has the given key signature. Begin on the tonic and remember to include any additional sharp, flat or natural signs.

(b) Write a key signature of four sharps and then one octave **descending** of the major scale which has that key signature. Use semibreves (whole-notes) and begin on the tonic.

(a) Compose a complete melody for unaccompanied oboe or trumpet, using the given opening. Indicate the tempo and other performance directions, including any that might be particularly required for the instrument chosen. The complete melody should be eight bars long.

Instrument for which the melody is written: ...........................................

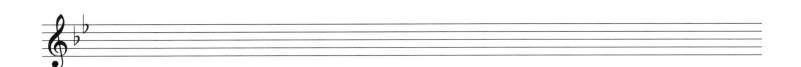

**OR**

(b) Compose a complete melody to the following words for a solo voice. Write each syllable under the note or notes to which it is to be sung. Also indicate the tempo and other performance directions as appropriate.

> The Sun does arise, and make happy the skies;
> The merry bells ring to welcome the Spring. *William Blake*

**7** Suggest suitable progressions for two cadences in the following melody by indicating ONLY ONE chord (I, II, IV or V) at each of the places marked A–E. You do not have to indicate the position of the chords, or to state which note is in the bass.

Show the chords:

EITHER   (a)  by writing I, II etc. or any other recognized symbols on the dotted lines below;

OR        (b)  by writing notes on the staves.

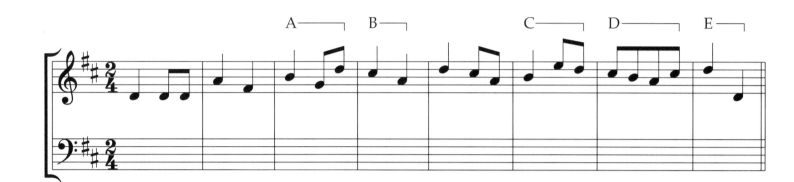

FIRST CADENCE:

Chord A   .................................................

Chord B   .................................................

SECOND CADENCE:

Chord C   .................................................

Chord D   .................................................

Chord E   .................................................

BLANK PAGE

# Theory Paper Grade 5   2008   B

*Duration 2 hours*

This paper contains SEVEN questions, ALL of which should be answered.
Write your answers on this paper – no others will be accepted.
Answers must be written clearly and neatly – otherwise marks may be lost.

15

**1** Look at this extract from a piano piece by Glinka and then answer the questions below.

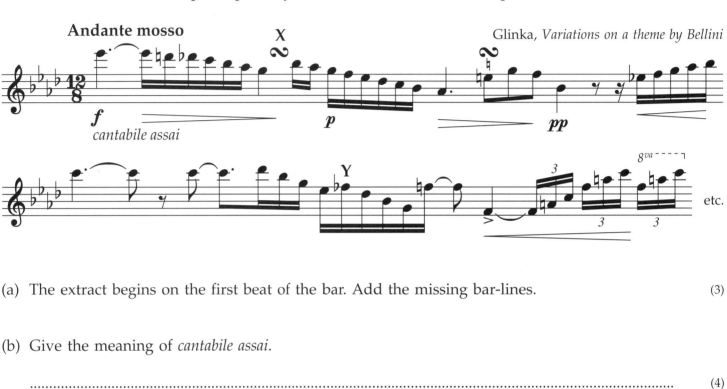

(a) The extract begins on the first beat of the bar. Add the missing bar-lines. (3)

(b) Give the meaning of *cantabile assai*.

............................................................................................................ (4)

(c) Describe the time signature as:   simple or compound  .............................................

duple, triple or quadruple  .................................. (2)

(d) Name the ornament marked **X**.  ............................................................. (2)

(e) Complete the following statement:

The $8^{va}$‐ ‐ ‐ ‐ ┐ sign in the final bar means .........................................................................

............................................................... . (2)

(f) Write as a breve (double whole-note) an enharmonic equivalent of the note marked **Y**.

(2)

**2** Describe fully each of the numbered melodic intervals (e.g. major 3rd).

J. S. Bach, Chorale Prelude 'Jesus Christus, unser Heiland', BWV 665

etc.

Intervals:

1 .............................................................

2 .............................................................

3 .............................................................

4 .............................................................

5 .............................................................

**3** The following melody is written for clarinet in A. Transpose it *down* a minor 3rd, as it will sound at concert pitch. Remember to put in the new key signature and add any necessary accidentals.

Brahms, Clarinet Quintet, Op. 115

etc.

**4** The following extract is from a piano sonata by Clementi. Look at it and then answer the questions that follow.

(a) (i) Give the meaning of:

┌─────────┐
│ 10      │
└─────────┘

**Adagio** ................................................................ (2)

*molto sostenuto* ......................................................................................................... (4)

*sf* (e.g. bar 4) ............................................................................................................. (2)

(ii) What do the two dots after the second right-hand note in bar 1 tell the player to do?

....................................................................................................................... (2)

(b) (i) The key of the extract is E major.

   [10]

   Which other key has the same key signature? .................................... (2)

(ii) **Mark clearly on the music**, using the appropriate capital letter for identification, one example of each of the following. Also give the bar number of each of your answers, as shown in the answer to **A**.

   **A** a submediant note in the right-hand
   part. Remember that the key is E major.  Bar ....2....

   **B** a tonic chord in second inversion (Ic).  Bar .......... (2)

   **C** a dominant chord in root position (Va).  Bar .......... (2)

   **D** an acciaccatura.  Bar .......... (2)

   **E** a turn.  Bar .......... (2)

(c) (i) Rewrite the first left-hand chord of bar 9 so that it sounds at the same pitch, but using the tenor C clef. Remember to put in the clef and the key signature.

   [10]

   (4)

(ii) Underline *one* of the following instruments that could play the right-hand part of the whole extract so that it sounds at the same pitch.

   bassoon          double bass          trombone          clarinet (2)

(iii) Now name a family of standard orchestral instruments that is *different* from the one to which the instrument you have underlined belongs, and state its highest-sounding member.

   Family ............................................          Instrument ............................................ (4)

**5** (a) Write the key signature of B major and then one octave **descending** of that scale. [10]
Use semibreves (whole-notes) and begin on the tonic.

(b) Write one octave **ascending** of the scale of F **harmonic** minor. Do *not* use a key signature but put in all necessary sharp or flat signs. Use semibreves (whole-notes) and begin on the tonic.

**6 EITHER**

(a) Compose a complete melody for unaccompanied cello or bassoon, using the given opening. Indicate the tempo and other performance directions, including any that might be particularly required for the instrument chosen. The complete melody should be eight bars long.

Instrument for which the melody is written: ...........................

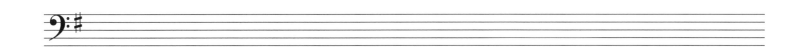

**OR**

(b) Compose a complete melody to the following words for a solo voice. Write each syllable under the note or notes to which it is to be sung. Also indicate the tempo and other performance directions as appropriate.

> But hark! the nightly Winds, with hollow Voice,
> Blow, blustering, from the South.           *James Thomson*

**7** Suggest suitable progressions for two cadences in the following melody by indicating 10 ONLY ONE chord (I, II, IV or V) at each of the places marked A–E. You do not have to indicate the position of the chords, or to state which note is in the bass.

Show the chords:

EITHER   (a)  by writing I, II etc. or any other recognized symbols on the dotted lines below;

OR   (b)  by writing notes on the staves.

FIRST CADENCE:

Chord A  .................................................

Chord B  .................................................

SECOND CADENCE:

Chord C  .................................................

Chord D  .................................................

Chord E  .................................................

BLANK PAGE

# Theory Paper Grade 5   2008   C

*Duration 2 hours*

This paper contains SEVEN questions, ALL of which should be answered.
Write your answers on this paper – no others will be accepted.
Answers must be written clearly and neatly – otherwise marks may be lost.

15

**1** (a) Look at the following extract and then answer the questions below.

Poglietti, Aria allemagna con alcuni variazioni

(i) Add the correct rest(s) at ✳ to complete the last bar. (2)

(ii) Rewrite the extract with the notes correctly grouped (beamed). (5)

(b) Look at the following extract and then answer the questions below.

Mozart, Piano Sonata in A, K. 331/300*i*

(i) Describe the chords marked ⟨A⟩ and ⟨B⟩ as I, II, IV or V. Also indicate whether the lowest note of the chord is the root (a), 3rd (b) or 5th (c). The key is A major.

Chord **A** .................................................... Chord **B** ........................................................ (4)

(ii) Below the staves write Ic–V ($^6_4$ $^5_3$) under the two successive chords where this progression occurs. (2)

(iii) Name another key that has the same key signature as A major. ......................................... (2)

**2** This passage is for SATB choir, written in short score. Rewrite it in open score.

10

Victoria, *Ne timeas, Maria*

etc.

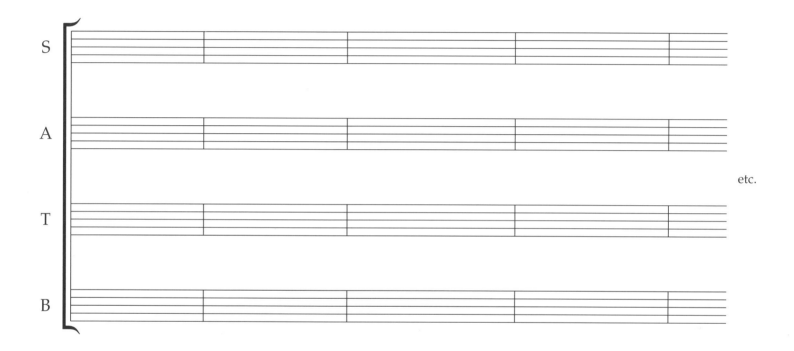

etc.

**3** Look at this extract from a sonata by Devienne, arranged for bassoon and piano, and then answer the questions printed opposite.

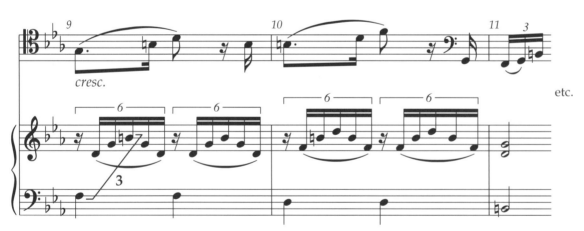

Adagio, from Sonata, Op. 24 No. 1
Music by François Devienne. Edited by William Waterhouse.
© Copyright 1977, 1992 Chester Music Ltd
All rights reserved. International Copyright Secured. Reproduced by permission.

(a) (i) Give the meaning of: [10]

**Adagio** ................................................................................................ (2)

♪=80 ................................................................................................ (2)

⌐—— 6 ——⌐ (e.g. bar 10, piano right hand) ..................................

.................................................................................................................... (2)

(ii) The extract begins in the key of E♭ major. Give the technical
name (e.g. tonic, dominant) of the last bassoon note in bar 1. ........................... (2)

(iii) Write as a breve (double whole-note) an enharmonic equivalent of the last left-hand
piano note in the extract.

(2)

(b) (i) Describe fully each of the numbered and bracketed harmonic intervals in the [10]
piano part (e.g. major 2nd).

**1** (bar 5, left-hand and bottom right-hand notes) ......................................... (2)

**2** (bar 7, left-hand and bottom right-hand notes) ......................................... (2)

**3** (bar 9, left-hand and right-hand notes) ......................................... (2)

(ii) Rewrite the first three notes of the bassoon part of bar 9 so that they sound at the
same pitch, but using the bass clef.

(2)

(iii) Complete the following statement: The extract begins in
the key of E♭ major, but at bar 6 it has moved to the key of ........................... . (2)

(c) (i) As the extract shows, the bassoon uses both the tenor C and bass clefs. [10]
Name a standard orchestral string instrument that also uses both these clefs.

Instrument .............................................. (2)

(ii) Underline *one* of the following instruments that could play bars 5–11 of the bassoon
part so that it sounds at the same pitch.

clarinet          trumpet          viola          trombone (2)

To which family of orchestral instruments
does the instrument you have underlined belong? ........................... (2)

(iii) Name two standard orchestral percussion instruments, one that produces notes of
definite pitch and one that produces notes of indefinite pitch.

Definite pitch ..............................     Indefinite pitch .............................. (4)

21

**4** (a) Put sharps or flats in front of the notes that need them to form the scale of F♯ **melodic** minor. Do *not* use a key signature.

(b) Write a key signature of four flats and then one octave **descending** of the major scale which has that key signature. Use semibreves (whole-notes) and begin on the tonic.

**5** These are the actual sounds made by a clarinet in B♭. Rewrite the passage as it would appear for the player to read, that is, transpose it *up* a major 2nd. Do *not* use a key signature but remember to put in all necessary sharp, flat or natural signs.

Reger, Clarinet Sonata No. 3 in B flat, Op. 107

**6  EITHER**

(a) Compose a complete melody for unaccompanied trumpet or flute, using the given opening. Indicate the tempo and other performance directions, including any that might be particularly required for the instrument chosen. The complete melody should be eight bars long.

Instrument for which the melody is written:  ...............................

**OR**

(b) Compose a complete melody to the following words for a solo voice. Write each syllable under the note or notes to which it is to be sung. Also indicate the tempo and other performance directions as appropriate.

> The merry brown hares came leaping
> Over the crest of the hill.                    *Charles Kingsley*

**7** Suggest suitable progressions for two cadences in the following melody by indicating ONLY ONE chord (I, II, IV or V) at each of the places marked A–E. You do not have to indicate the position of the chords, or to state which note is in the bass.

Show the chords:

EITHER    (a)  by writing I, II etc. or any other recognized symbols on the dotted lines below;

OR        (b)  by writing notes on the staves.

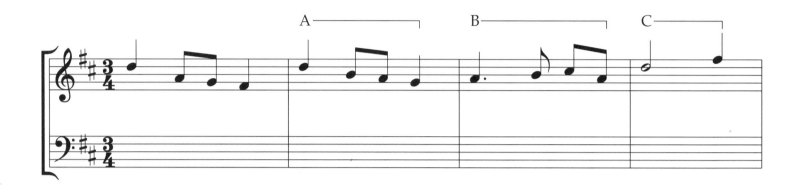

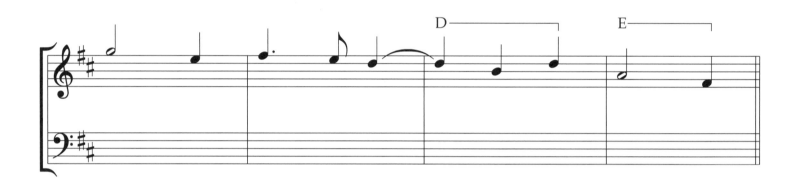

FIRST CADENCE:                                    SECOND CADENCE:

Chord A  ...............................................

                                                  Chord D  ...............................................

Chord B  ...............................................

                                                  Chord E  ...............................................

Chord C  ...............................................

BLANK PAGE

# Theory Paper Grade 5   2008   S

*Duration 2 hours*

**This paper contains SEVEN questions, ALL of which should be answered.**
**Write your answers on this paper – no others will be accepted.**
**Answers must be written clearly and neatly – otherwise marks may be lost.**

**1** (a) Look at the following extract, which begins on the first beat of the bar and contains some changes of time signature, and then answer the questions below.

15

Stravinsky, *The Rite of Spring*

etc.   © Copyright 1912, 1921 by Hawkes & Son (London) Ltd
Reproduced by permission of Boosey & Hawkes Music Publishers Ltd.

(i) Put in the three correct time signatures at the places marked ✳. (6)

(ii) Add the correct rest(s) to bar 3 to complete the bar. (2)

(iii) Rewrite the last two notes of the extract above so that they sound at the same pitch, but using the bass clef.

(2)

(b) The following extract begins on the first beat of the bar. Put in the correct time-signature at the beginning and add the missing bar-lines. The first bar-line is given. (5)

Haydn, Piano Sonata in A, Hob. XVI/26

etc.

26

**2** Describe fully each of the numbered melodic intervals (e.g. major 2nd).

Balakirev, Sonata for piano

Intervals:

1 .................................................

2 .................................................

3 .................................................

4 .................................................

5 .................................................

**3** The following melody is written for trumpet in B♭. Transpose it *down* a major 2nd, as it will sound at concert pitch. Do *not* use a key signature but remember to put in all necessary sharp, flat or natural signs.

Shostakovich, Symphony No. 8

etc.

**4** Look at this extract adapted from a song, *Der Jüngling in der Fremde*, by Beethoven and then answer the questions that follow.

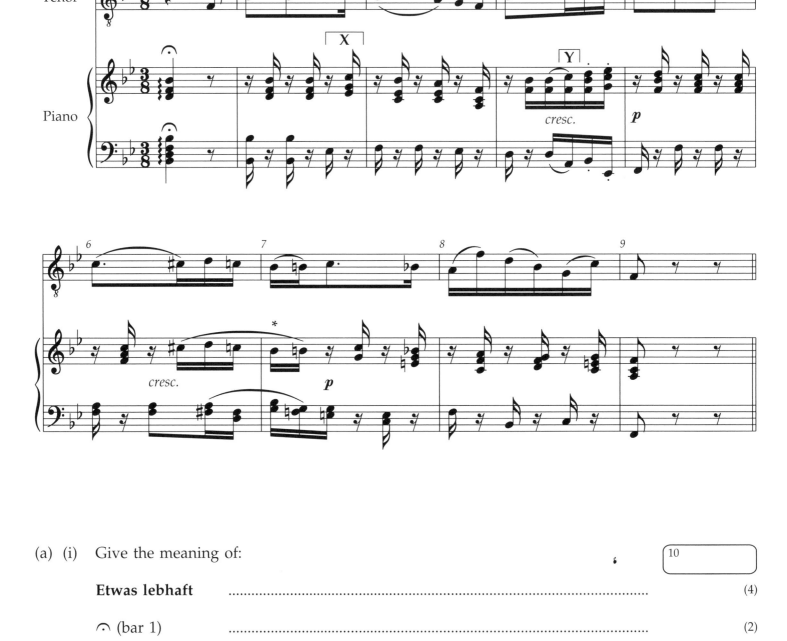

(a) (i) Give the meaning of:

**Etwas lebhaft** ...................................................................................................................... (4)

⌢ (bar 1) ...................................................................................................................... (2)

𝄾 (bar 1, piano) ...................................................................................................................... (2)

(ii) The extract begins in the key of B♭ major. In what key does it end? ................................ (2)

(b) (i) Describe the chords in the piano part marked ⌐X⌐ and ⌐Y⌐ as I, II, IV or V. Also indicate whether the lowest note of the chord is the root (a), 3rd (b) or 5th (c). The key is B♭ major.

⌐10⌐

Chord **X** (bar 2)  ..................................................................................... (2)

Chord **Y** (bar 4)  ..................................................................................... (2)

(ii) Below the staves write Ic–V ($^6_4$ $^5_3$) under the two successive chords where this progression occurs. (2)

(iii) Write as a breve (double whole-note) an enharmonic equivalent of the first right-hand piano note of bar 7 (marked ∗).

(2)

(iv) Draw a circle round a note *in the voice part* that is the submediant of the scale of B♭ major. (2)

(c) (i) The extract is written for the tenor voice. Give the name of the voice part which lies between tenor and bass in vocal range.

⌐10⌐

...................................... (2)

(ii) Underline *one* of the following instruments that could play bars 3–5 of the left-hand piano part so that it sounds at the same pitch.

        oboe         trumpet         viola         bassoon (2)

To which family of orchestral instruments does the instrument you have underlined belong?

...................................................... (2)

(iii) Now name a *different* family of standard orchestral instruments and state its highest-sounding member.

Family  .....................................     Instrument  ..................................... (4)

**5** (a) Write a key signature of three sharps and then one octave **ascending** of the **harmonic**  minor scale which has that key signature. Use semibreves (whole-notes), begin on the tonic and remember to put in any additional sharp, flat or natural signs.

(b) Using semibreves (whole-notes), write one octave **descending** of the major scale that begins on the given note. Do *not* use a key signature but put in all necessary sharp or flat signs.

## 6 EITHER

(a) Compose a complete melody for unaccompanied violin or oboe, using the given opening. Indicate the tempo and other performance directions, including any that might be particularly required for the instrument chosen. The complete melody should be eight bars long.

Instrument for which the melody is written: ...............................................

OR

(b) Compose a complete melody to the following words for a solo voice. Write each syllable under the note or notes to which it is to be sung. Also indicate the tempo and other performance directions as appropriate.

> This City now doth, like a garment, wear
> The beauty of the morning.
> *William Wordsworth*

7 Suggest suitable progressions for two cadences in the following melody by indicating ONLY ONE chord (I, II, IV or V) at each of the places marked A–E. You do not have to indicate the position of the chords, or to state which note is in the bass.

Show the chords:

EITHER    (a) by writing I, II etc. or any other recognized symbols on the dotted lines below;

OR       (b) by writing notes on the staves.

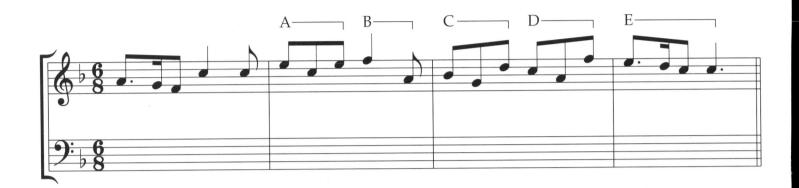

FIRST CADENCE:

Chord A  ....................................................

Chord B  ....................................................

SECOND CADENCE:

Chord C  ....................................................

Chord D  ....................................................

Chord E  ....................................................

*Theory of Music Exams Model Answers*, 2008 are available now from your usual retailer.

Grade 1  978-1-86096-981-2
Grade 2  978-1-86096-982-9
Grade 3  978-1-86096-983-6
Grade 4  978-1-86096-984-3
Grade 5  978-1-86096-985-0
Grade 6  978-1-86096-986-7
Grade 7  978-1-86096-987-4
Grade 8  978-1-86096-988-1

**ABRSM**
24 Portland Place
London W1B 1LU
United Kingdom

www.abrsm.org

ISBN 978-1-86096-965-2

Published by ABRSM (Publishing) Ltd, a wholly owned subsidiary of ABRSM
Printed in England by Halstan & Co. Ltd, Amersham, Bucks 08/09